SPACE
RESCUE

CREATED AND PRODUCED by
Firecrest Books Ltd in association with Graham White

First published in Great Britain in 2001 by Simon & Schuster UK Ltd,
Africa House, 64-78 Kingsway, London WC2B 6AH.
A Viacom company.

ISBN 0689 836392

A CIP catalogue record for this book is available
from the British Library upon request.

PUBLISHING CONSULTANT Peter Sackett

DESIGNED by Phil Jacobs

EDITED by Norman Barrett

PROJECT CO-ORDINATOR Pat Jacobs

Colour separation in Singapore by Sang Choy International Pte Ltd

Printed in Belgium by Casterman Printers

...the image that downloaded onto the screen was
awesome – the twisted wreckage of a space freighter lay
tangled in the dense jungle of an alien planet...

You're a lively – and bored – kid living in the future, where life is easy but dull, and there's little to challenge
your adventurous young mind. Sitting in the Cybernet Café one day, idly surfing the net, you stumble upon a
website that makes you leap out of your seat with excitement . . .

-- SOS -- SOS -- SOS -- SOS -- SOS -- SOS -- SOS -- SOS -- SOS -- SOS -- SOS -- SOS --

This is a call for urgent assistance from the crew of space freighter C1-83724. We are stranded on
planet G45 in the Durain system, where we were due to deliver supplies of nuclear explosives to the
mining colony. During the landing sequence our vessel went out of control, crashing to the east of
the settlement. Our explosives became unstable on impact and are fast reaching a critical state. If
this lot blows, it will wipe out the whole planet! The inhabitants have teleported to safety, but
we have to remain here to monitor the temperature of the explosives. We are running low on coolant
and our only hope is to get back to the space station where they can be made safe. Our emergency
escape shuttle is still operational, but our Nav-PATH key has been damaged in the crash.

-- SOS -- SOS -- SOS -- SOS -- SOS -- SOS -- SOS -- SOS -- SOS -- SOS --SOS -- SOS -- SOS

A quick search on the net reveals that Nav-PATH stands for Navigation Particle Avoidance Track-Holding, and this key must, according to regulation
F193 of the Space Directorate Assembly, be locked into the navigation computer of any ship carrying volatile material to ensure its safe passage
through space with zero risk of collision. Without it, the emergency shuttle is useless. Convinced that the fate of both the crew and the planet lies in
your hands, you decide to mount your own single-handed rescue mission.

CONTENTS

Attention all space rescuers!

Your adventure can be completed in an infinite number of ways. The ultimate objective is to find the shortest route. When you have completed the rescue for the first time, try again to see if you can improve on your previous attempt and eventually find the quickest route (revealed at the end of the book). Why not compete with a friend to see who succeeds in the shortest time?

How to use the mazes

The City
Begin your rescue mission in a labyrinth of streets and walkways. Find your way across town to the airport on the outskirts.

The Airport
A futuristic passenger plane awaits your arrival to transport you to Mission Control. Your problem is to find your way to your seat!

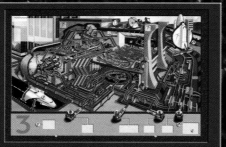

Mission Control
You cannot go into space without training! Find your way to the shuttle by passing through all the rigorous preparation procedures.

The Lifts
Can you beat security by using the lifts in the correct sequence to board the shuttle?

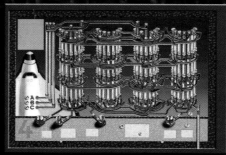

The Shuttle
Now you're making real progress! You will soon arrive at the space station — but as you make your way to the docking bay, you catch a glimpse of the beautiful planet Earth behind you and wonder if you will return safely.

So there it is — your whole journey. But hey! You didn't think it was going to be that easy did you? To complete the rescue successfully you must use some of the many teleports that transport you through space and time. You may even find yourself transported to parts of your journey you haven't even reached yet! Oh . . . and we mustn't forget to mention those gates which block your way . . . unless you've opened them beforehand of course!

How to use the mazes

Here is a simple maze which includes everything you may come across on your travels. Take a few moments before you begin your journey to familiarise yourself with the symbols.

Travel instructions

 You will need a notebook and pencil (your "logbook").

 There are no dead-ends so just keep going — you will always find a way forward if you look for it. You will only ever have to turn back and retrace your steps if you come to a gate you haven't opened or you reach an incoming teleport pod at the bottom of the page.

 You will know if you have taken a wrong turning somewhere along your journey if you find yourself back at part of the maze you've travelled before — but just carry on and look for a route you may have missed.

 When you come across a yellow signpost (signalled by a round red marker on your route), look at the bottom of the page for a reminder of what the sign means.

 And one more thing — no cheating! You may not pass through closed gates, hop over walls, swim across rivers, cross yellow and black lines, throw yourself from one level to another or run over the grass . . . and definitely no peeking at the solution and telling everyone you didn't!

So off you go! The first step is to find [footprint symbol] on Maze 1 (pages 8-9). You are on your way. Good luck!

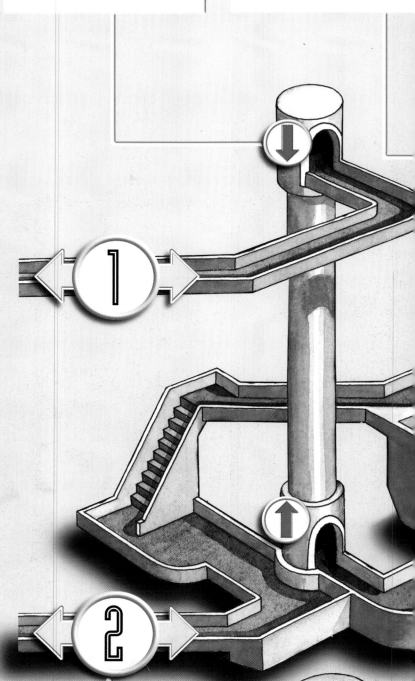

Lift arrows: enter the lift at the top or bottom and travel down or up until you reach the other arrow, where you will find the exit.

Start at the red marker leading from the footprint sign if you have completed the previous maze and have just turned the page.

If you come to a symbol like this, simply continue your journey over to the previous page, following the same numbered route as indicated.

This is an exit teleport pod. When you come to one of these, you must teleport to another maze. Instructions alongside will tell you where to go.

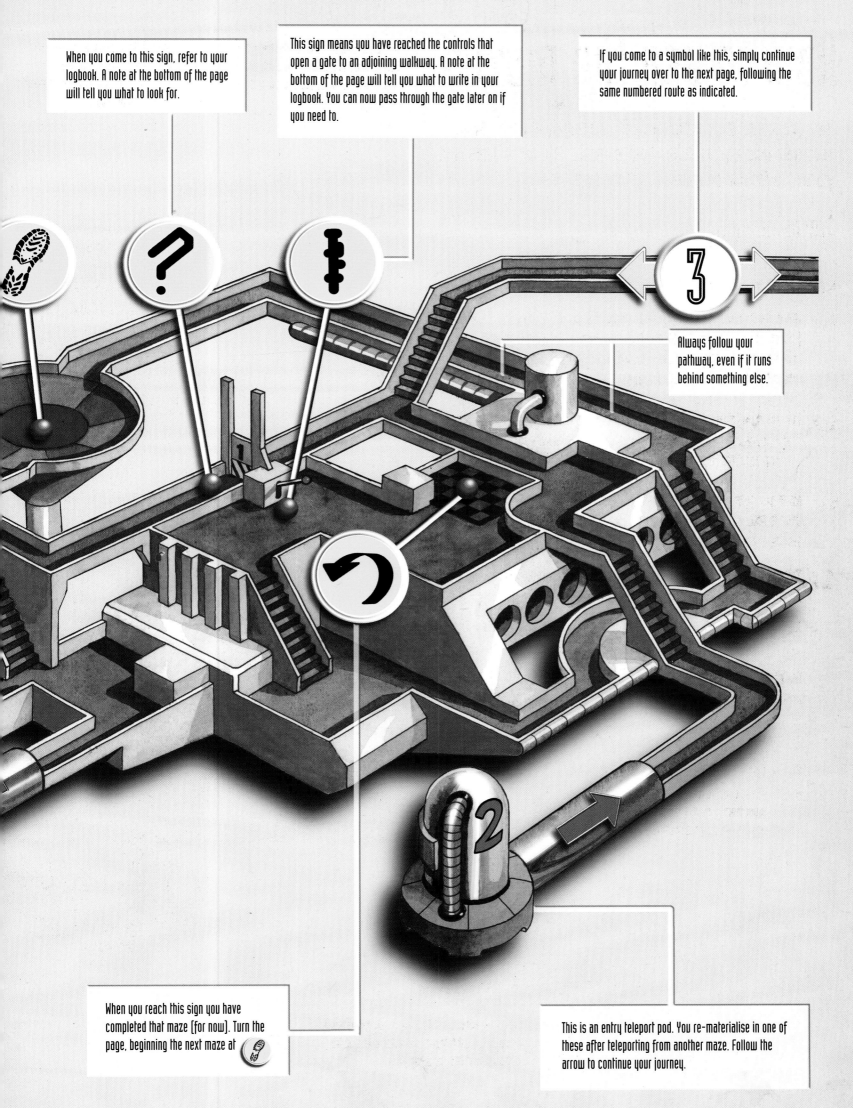

When you come to this sign, refer to your logbook. A note at the bottom of the page will tell you what to look for.

This sign means you have reached the controls that open a gate to an adjoining walkway. A note at the bottom of the page will tell you what to write in your logbook. You can now pass through the gate later on if you need to.

If you come to a symbol like this, simply continue your journey over to the next page, following the same numbered route as indicated.

Always follow your pathway, even if it runs behind something else.

When you reach this sign you have completed that maze (for now). Turn the page, beginning the next maze at

This is an entry teleport pod. You re-materialise in one of these after teleporting from another maze. Follow the arrow to continue your journey.

Maze 1. The City

You have just received the internet message and are about to begin your adventure. Have you got your logbook ready? Then let's go! Your first task is to get across town to the Airport, using one of the exits on the right. Don't worry if you come to a teleporter at the bottom of the page and have to leave the City early — it could be just what you need to do!

Oh dear . . . you have returned unsuccessfully. Try again!

Teleport to Maze 2 (The Airport). Materialise in pod 1.

Start your mission here.

Make a note in your logbook that you have opened gate No. 1.

Refer to your logbook. Have you previously opened gate No. 1? If so, you may pass. If not . . . back you go!

Teleport to Maze 7
(The Mining Colony).
Materialise in pod 2.

Maze 2. The Airport

Look at the size of that aeroplane! Luckily you managed to acquire a valid one-way ticket to Mission Control from a friend on the internet (you didn't ask where he got it from), so you won't have to stow away. Instead you can make your way to your special seat on the observation deck, marked 🔄

The way there could be farther than you think!

Welcome to the Airport. We hope we have reassembled all your molecules correctly!

Welcome to the Airport. The tingling in your toes will wear off shortly.

Teleport to Maze 6 [The Space Station]. Materialise in pod 3.

Welcome to the Airport. Oops! Your shirt has changed colour. It looks better now.

Congratulations! You have found your seat. Did you do any teleporting on the way? Now that you have completed this maze (for now at least), you can sit back and enjoy the flight to Mission Control.

Turn the page and you will find that this bird flies so fast that you have landed there already! Start your new maze at

Maze 3. Mission Control

Wow! This looks like a busy place!

Now you have to learn as much as you can about space flight, so take a wander round while trying to make your way to the space shuttle. You may pass through the underwater training tank, the flight simulator, the control room, the labs, the gym, or even endure 7Gs on the centrifuge. Wow, these astronauts have to go through an awful lot! Maybe it wouldn't be such a bad idea if you teleported to another maze . . .

FLIGHT SIMULATOR

TRAINING TANK

GYMNASIUM

3

That was a quick flight! Leave the plane from this door please.

Teleport to Maze 1 (The City). Materialise in pod 5.

5

CONTROL ROOM

CENTRIFUGE

LABS

FUEL LINES

Welcome to Mission Control. Turn right for a quick route to the shuttle lifts, left for an exciting training tour.

Teleport to Maze 4 [The Lifts]. Materialise in pod 4.

Teleport to Maze 7 [The Mining Colony]. Materialise in pod 2.

Yes! Your training is complete. Now you must turn the page to encounter the lift security system. Start at when you get there.

Maze 4. The Lifts

No doubt this will be an uplifting experience for you!

For security reasons, these lifts will only take you up or down one level at a time. It doesn't matter if you go up or down, but you must remember to step out of your lift at the next level and follow the walkway to a new one. If you beat security, you will arrive either at the shuttle or a teleporter.

We have lift-off!

A

B

C

Teleport to Maze 2 (The Airport). Materialise in pod 1.

Welcome to the Lifts. Please use the handrails. You may be a little unsteady on your feet after teleporting.

Welcome to the Lifts. Your transfer has been perfect.

Well done! You have reached a shuttle entrance —
but which one? Make a note of your entrance letter
(A, B or C), then turn the page to the next maze,
The Shuttle. You must enter the shuttle by
the same entrance (marked 👣).

Teleport to Maze 9
(The Stricken Spaceship).
Materialise in pod 7.

Start here and
remember, we all have
our ups and downs.

Maze 5. The Shuttle

Now that really is a room with a view! Good job you're not scared of heights.

You must quickly make your way to the docking bay [marked 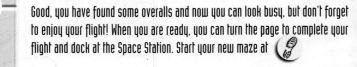], where you can find some overalls and mingle without being noticed. If you come across a teleport substation, just follow the beam to your teleporter at the bottom of the page — it will take you somewhere a little firmer underfoot which may [or may not] help you later on.

5

Now boarding the Shuttle! Space sickness pills are available if you need them. We hope you have a pleasant journey.

Good, you have found some overalls and now you can look busy, but don't forget to enjoy your flight! When you are ready, you can turn the page to complete your flight and dock at the Space Station. Start your new maze at

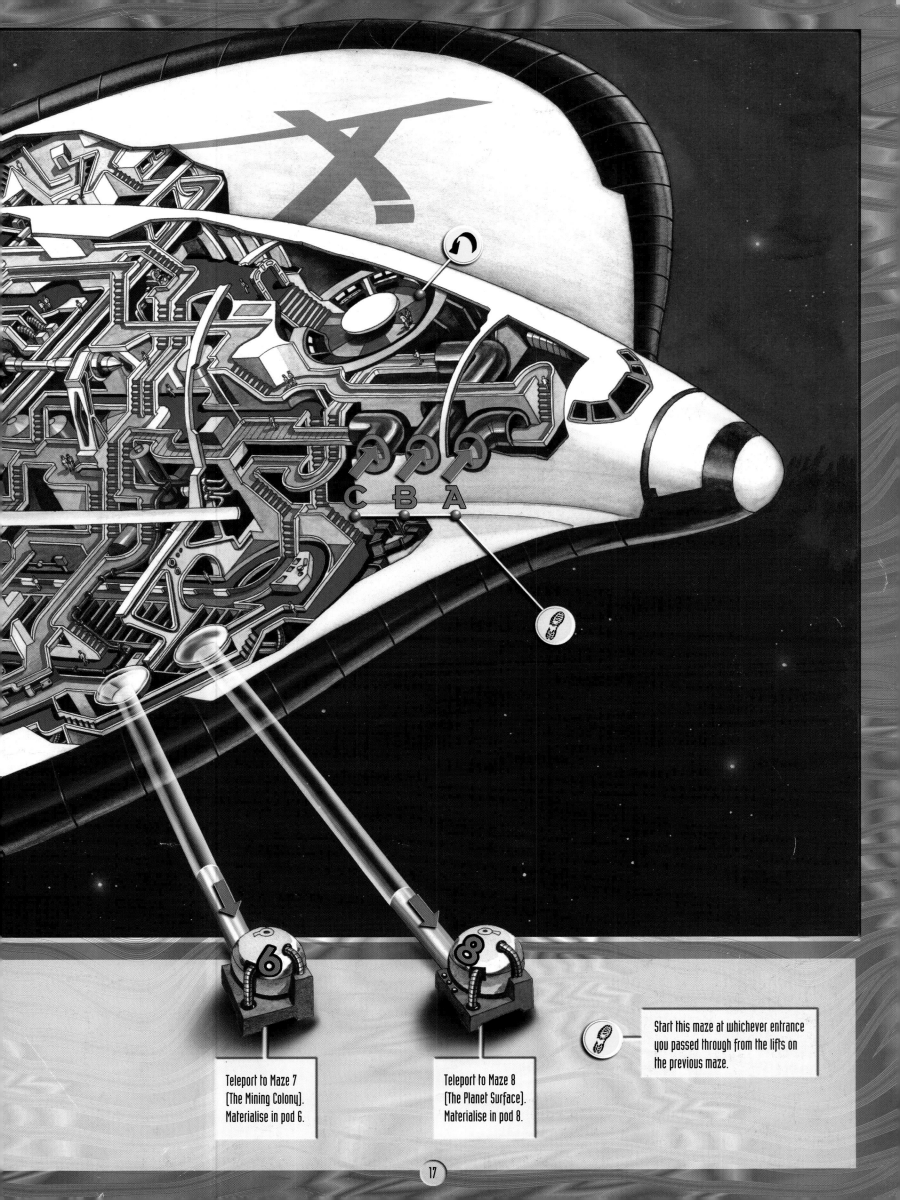

C B A

Teleport to Maze 7
(The Mining Colony).
Materialise in pod 6.

Teleport to Maze 8
(The Planet Surface).
Materialise in pod 8.

Start this maze at whichever entrance
you passed through from the lifts on
the previous maze.

Maze 6. The Space Station

Make sure your magnetic boots are switched on — you will need them in this crazy construction! Up here there is no 'right way up', so to keep your feet pointing downwards, you'll have to turn the book around as you go. Make your way to either the control room marked ⟲ where you will find the Nav-PATH key, or to one of the three exit teleporters.

Teleport to Maze 3 [Mission Control]. Materialise in pod 10.

Teleport to Maze 7 [The Mining Colony]. Materialise in pod 2.

Welcome to the Space Station. Oops! You have materialised upside-down — but it makes no difference here.

Well done! You have found your way to the control room at last. The Nav-PATH key is ready to be programmed, so take a seat and put your thinking cap on. Now turn the page to find out what to do.

Teleport to Maze 2 (The Airport). Materialise in pod 9.

The shuttle has docked, so without being noticed you can board the Space Station here.

Make a note in your logbook that you have opened gate No. 2.

Refer to your logbook. Have you opened gate No. 2? If so, you may pass. If not, take another route.

The PATH key

It's time to program your Navigation PATH key!
First you have to program 15 DIRECTION changes.
Then you need to program 15 DISTANCES, one for
each direction. But before you start, draw this in
your logbook:

This row of boxes is for DIRECTION ▼

This row of boxes is for DISTANCES ▲

There should be two rows of 15 squares.
Now you are ready to program
your PATH key.

Travel from A to B

Symbols to enter
in logbook

How to program your DIRECTIONS:

On the PATH key you will see a weird-looking electric circuit with many
funny- shaped components connected by the gold strips on the board. Two
components are labelled A and B. Can you find them? Good! Now you must find
a way from A to B by following the gold circuit.

Now go back to your logbook and draw the components, in order, along the top row,
one in each box. The diagram next to the key shows you how to draw each one
easily. Your first box should look like this

[To do this correctly you should pass 15 components as you go.]

You have now programmed the DIRECTIONS into your PATH key.

The Space Chart

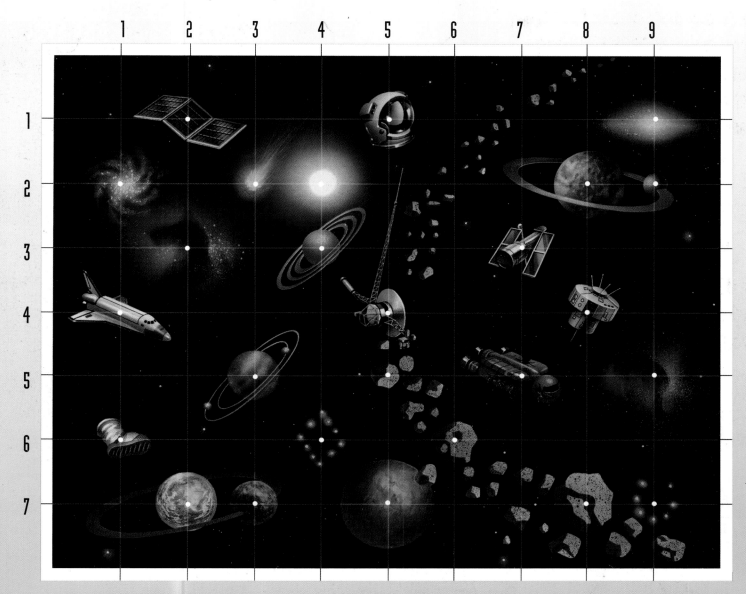

1 A planet similar to Earth
2 A space probe with a long antenna
3 A planet with three rings
4 The largest moon
5 An old-type space shuttle
6 A spaceman's helmet floating free
7 A solar panel floating free
8 An abandoned spaceship wreck
9 A spiral galaxy
10 The largest asteroid
11 The planet with two moons
12 The nebula shaped like a horse's head
13 The nearest star to Earth
14 A constellation in the shape of a horseshoe
15 A comet

Teleport to Maze 7 (The Mining Colony). Materialise in pod 15.

How to program the DISTANCES:

You must now identify the objects on the Space Chart. Start with question 1 and find the planet which is similar to Earth. Look at the figures around the edge of the chart. If you have chosen correctly your planet should be here

The co-ordinates of your planet are 7, 2.

Now simply add these two numbers together and your final DISTANCE number is 9.

This is the first number in your bottom row of boxes

Now answer each of the other questions, adding up the two co-ordinates to give you a DISTANCE number for each. Write your 15 numbers, in order, in the bottom row of boxes in your logbook. You have now completely programmed your Navigation PATH key. Keep this information safe — you will need it for your journey home. It's time to continue your mission now, so off you go to the Mining Colony using the teleport No. 15 above.

Maze 7. The Mining Colony

This journey has suddenly got a bit spooky! It's very dark down here, deep below ground. Even the slightest sound echoes in the deserted passages.

It's a good job there are plenty of ways out. You'd be well-advised to leave as soon as possible by one of the exits on the right or by jumping into an exit teleporter at the bottom.

Hurry now! Alien creatures may have made this place their new home.

Welcome to the Mining Colony. Please walk slowly for a while until you get used to solid ground again.

Welcome to the Mining Colony. Try not to touch the damp walls. The smell on your hands will last for ages.

Welcome to the Mining Colony. Oops! It looks like a bit too much teleport energy was used on you. You're glowing in the dark!

5

6

7

8

9

11

13

9

Teleport to Maze 2
(The Airport).
Materialise in pod 11.

Welcome to the Mining Colony.
The teleport travel sickness will
wear off in 15 seconds.

Teleport to Maze 2
(The Airport).
Materialise in pod 9.

Make a note in your logbook that you
have opened gate No. 3.

Refer to your logbook. Have you
previously opened gate No. 3? If so, you
may pass. If not . . . try another route.

Maze 8. The Planet Surface

My goodness! Suddenly those astronauts seem farther away than you thought. But don't despair . . . there may be an easier way to reach them by getting to another maze quickly.

Try climbing your way out of this one by reaching one of the exits on either side, or by teleporting from a pod at the bottom.

We hope you get there before your boots wear out!

5

6

7

8

9

?

12

13

Teleport to Maze 5 [The Shuttle]. Materialise in pod 12.

Teleport to Maze 7 [The Mining Colony]. Materialise in pod 13.

Make a note in your logbook that you have opened gate No. 4.

Refer to your logbook. Have you previously opened gate No. 4? If so, you may pass. If not . . . back you go!

Welcome to the Planet Surface. To help with your climbing, a little extra energy has been added to your molecules.

Teleport to Maze 4 [The Lifts]. Materialise in pod 14.

Maze 9. The Stricken Spaceship

Oh dear! This ship won't be flying again! At least the emergency shuttle has survived, but getting to it could be a problem. The two astronauts sense that they could be rescued soon, but don't worry if you have to travel to another page before you reach them — you know by now that sometimes it's quicker that way.

Will this be your moment of glory. . . ?

10

11

12

13

14

5

4

9

Make a note in your logbook that you have opened gate No. 5.

Refer to your logbook. Have you opened gate No. 5?
If so, you may pass. If not. . .try another route.

Teleport to Maze 1
[The City].
Materialise in pod 5.

Teleport to Maze 4
[The Lifts].
Materialise in pod 4.

Teleport to Maze 8
(The Planet Surface).
Materialise in pod 8.

Welcome to the Stricken Spaceship.
What a mess! Suddenly, teleporting
seems a safe way to travel!

RESCUE!

Well done! You have reached the astronauts at last. All they have to do now is
plug your Nav-PATH key into the navigation computer and a safe journey home
is assured . . . or is it? Turn the page and use your program to plot your flight
back. Hold onto your seat, your adventure isn't over yet!

The Journey Home

At last it's time to return! You must fly your ship through the Space Sector back to the Space Station, but you must avoid all the planets and space-junk on your way. Are you ready? Then let's go!

START

Direction Module

The Direction Module on the left has six different directions, each indicated by a symbol. Recognise them? If you refer to your logbook, you will notice that these symbols match the ones you have drawn in the top row of your PATH key program.

FINISH

Look at the first pair of boxes in your program

9

Starting at the green symbol on the planet, you now travel nine spaces in direction ∩

You are on your way home! Continue your journey using the next pair of boxes and so on, until (hopefully) you reach the Space Station.

Good luck!

The Solutions

It's OK, all those crazy mazes haven't made your eyes go funny — we printed the solutions upside-down and back-to-front, just in case you were tempted to have a quick peek. If you really want to know the shortest route, you will need a mirror. Just hold it facing you at the top of each maze, and all will be revealed. So how did you do?

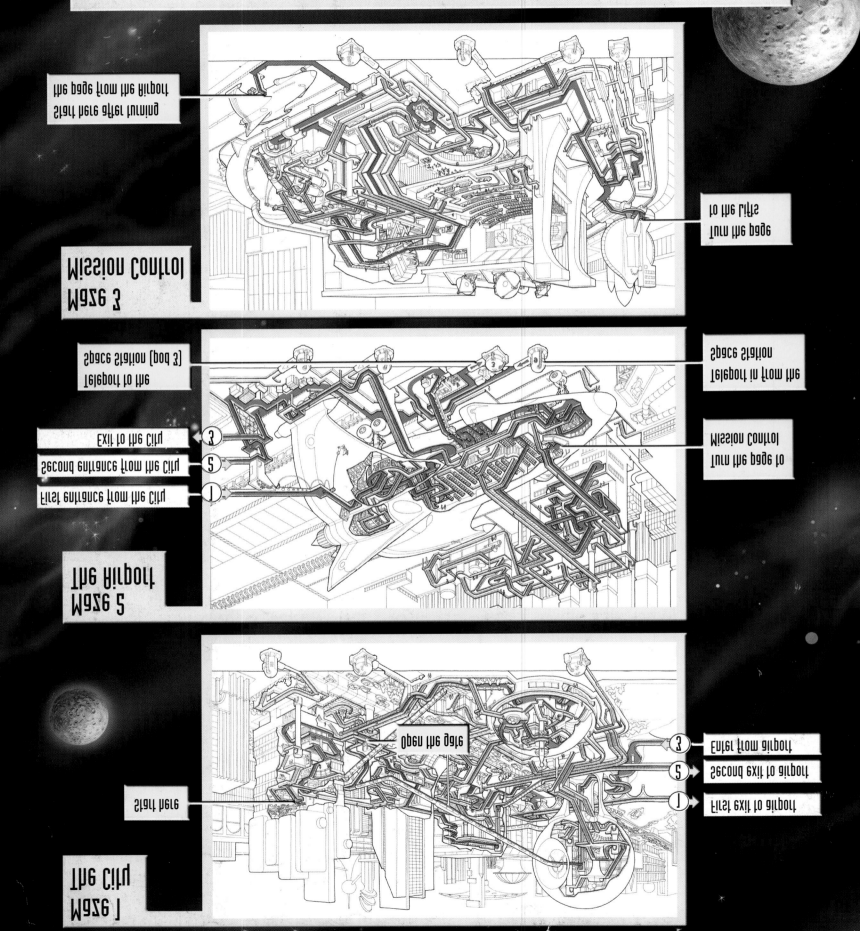

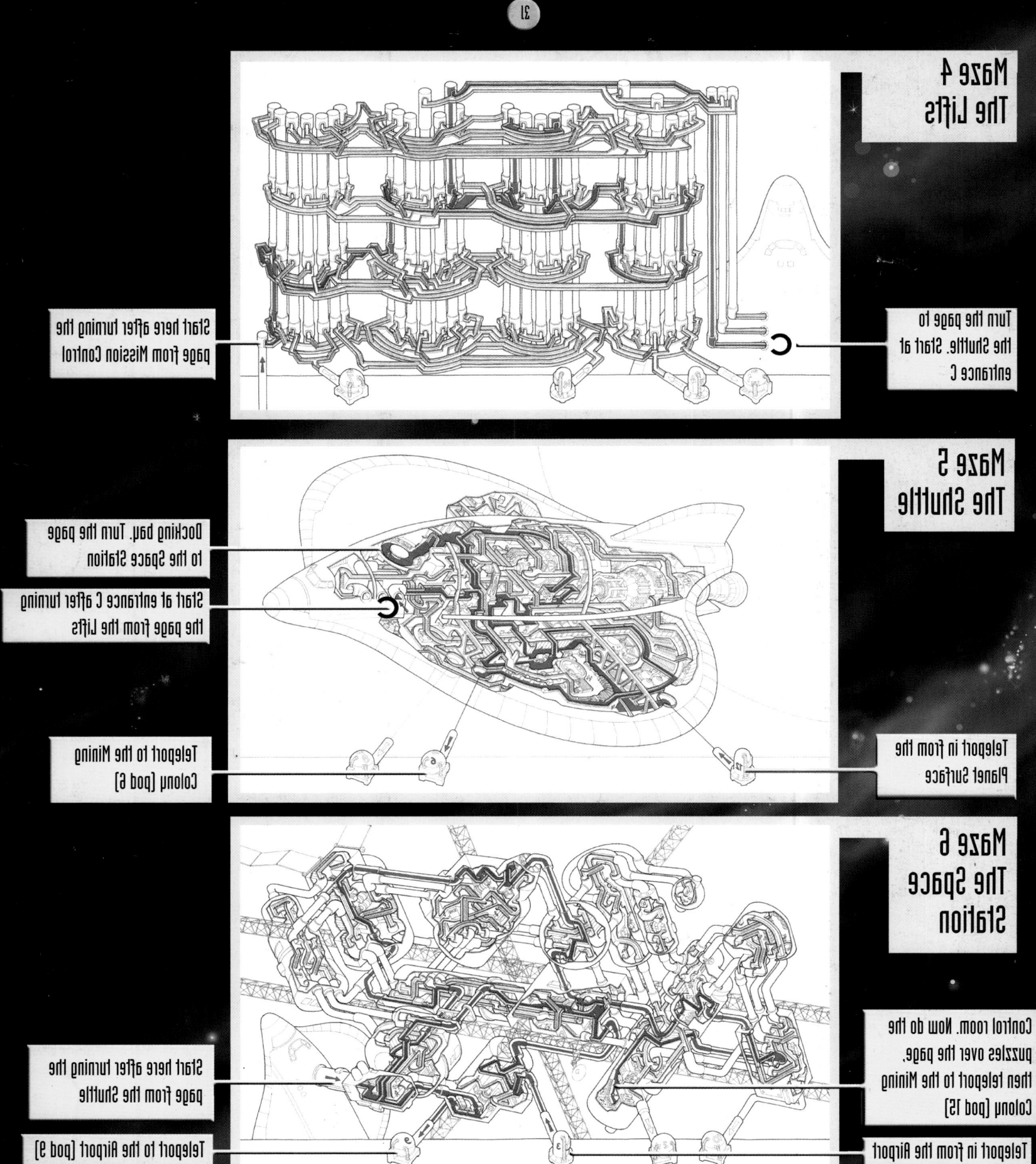

Maze 4
The Lifts

Turn the page to the Shuttle. Start at entrance C

Start here after turning the page from Mission Control

Maze 5
The Shuttle

Docking bay. Turn the page to the Space Station

Start at entrance C after turning the page from the Lifts

Teleport to the Mining Colony (pod 6)

Teleport in from the planet Surface

Maze 6
The Space Station

Control room. Now do the puzzles over the page, then teleport to the Mining Colony (pod 15)

Start here after turning the page from the Shuttle

Teleport to the Airport (pod 9)

Teleport in from the Airport

The Path Key

9	7	10	5	6	3	12	3	15	8	5	16	5

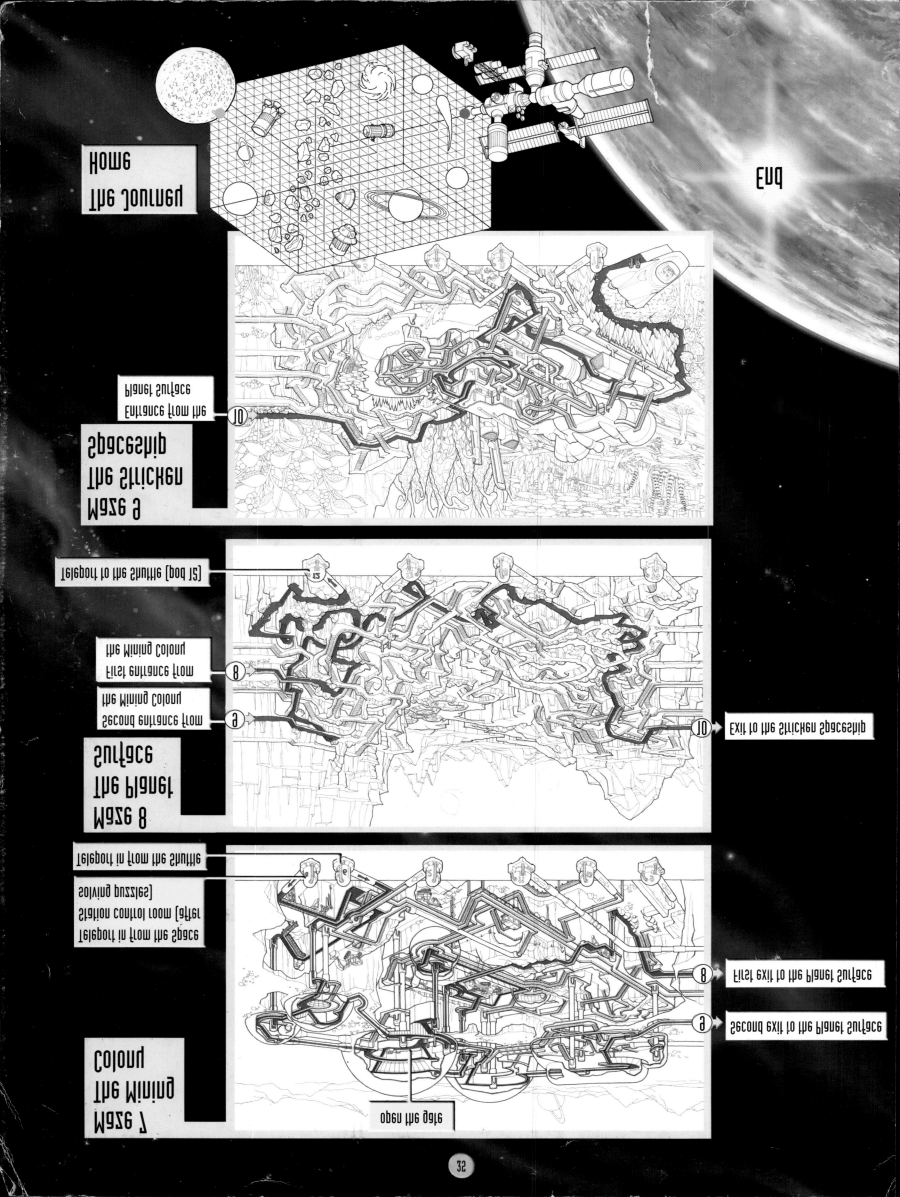